Spotlight on
Darwin and Evolution

David Barnaby

Cassell Graded Readers Level 6

General Editor: Michael Carrier

Cassell

London

CASSELL LTD
1 St Anne's Road, Eastbourne
East Sussex BN21 3UN

First published 1984

British Library Cataloguing in Publication Data

Barnaby, David
    Spotlight on Darwin and evolution. – (Cassell's
    spotlight readers)
    1. English language – Text-books for foreign
    speakers   2. Readers – Darwin, Charles
    I. Title
    428.6'4   PE1128

    ISBN 0-304-30824-2

Typeset by Inforum Ltd, Portsmouth
Printed in Hungary
Illustrations by Alice Englander

Grateful acknowledgement for permission to use photographs
reproduced in this book is made to the following (numbers
refer to the pages in the book on which they occur):

Tony Stone Associates (Cover)
Down House and Royal College of Surgeons of England (44)
British Tourist Authority (11)

Contents

Preface   v
Introduction   1

1   Erasmus Darwin   3
2   The early life of Charles Darwin   9
3   The *Beagle*   21
4   South America   27
5   Robert Fitzroy   34
6   The Galapagos Islands   38
7   Down House   43
8   Alfred Wallace   49
9   *The Origin of Species*   54
10 Gregor Mendel   60
11 Extinction   65

Exercises   71
Glossary   78
Appendix 1   85
Appendix 2   89

CASSELL GRADED READERS

ELEMENTARY
Spotlight on

Level 1
(350 headwords)
A Doctor's Day
Illusions
Muhammad Ali
A Radio Station
The World Cup
The British Royal Family
North Sea Oil
Parliament

Level 2
(700 headwords)
The Beginning of Radio
Inventions
British Food
Tennis
How a Record is Made
Great Mysteries
Assassins
The Space Race

INTERMEDIATE
Spotlight on

Level 3
(1050 headwords)
Motor Racing
Football
The Kennedys
The Common Market
Rock Music
Airports
The City
Tomorrow's World

Level 4
(1400 headwords)
Surprises of Nature
William Shakespeare
Strange Stories
Fleet Street
The Supernatural
Energy
Islam
The Olympics

ADVANCED
Spotlight on

Level 5
(1750 headwords)
The Pop Industry
British Theatre
Social Class in Britain
Cinema

Level 6
(2100 headwords)
The English Revolution
Winston Churchill
Women in Society
Darwin and Evolution

Preface

This is a new series of readers for foreign students of English. It is new in several ways. Firstly, it has been designed as a series rather than an arbitrary group of titles. Secondly, the series provides reading material that is representative of the students' interests and corresponds as far as possible to the books that students would read in their own language. Thus it consists only of informative, entertaining, non-fiction topics. Thirdly, the language used in the readers has been carefully chosen and controlled so as to be easily understandable for students without being childish or patronising in its tone. At the same time each reader introduces a sizeable amount of subject-specific vocabulary which would not normally be included in a simple grading system. This subject-specific vocabulary is carefully explained through text, illustration or glossary so that the student can deal with topics in a more serious and informative way.

There are six levels, Level 1 being the simplest and Level 6 the most difficult. Each level introduces *circa* 350 new headwords and the length of each reader depends on its level (see list of titles on facing page).

The language is controlled lexically according to a grading system, and subject-specific vocabulary is added where appropriate. There is also a structural grading which keeps syntactic complexity to a level that is comprehensible to the student. This operates mainly in Levels 1–4.

Because one of the main aims of Cassell's Graded Readers is to stimulate the student's interest and motivation to read, the books are presented in a lively and interesting format and are well-illustrated throughout. Each book also contains follow-up exercises and activities to give students the opportunity to take their interest in the topic, as well as in the language, further than a merely passive reading of the text.

Further details of the linguistic grading can be found in the Teacher's Guide to the series, obtainable from the publishers.

Michael Carrier
General Editor

Introduction

Charles Darwin was born in 1809. At that time, most people in Europe belonged to the Christian religion, and believed that the Christian Bible* gave the true story of the beginning of the world, the creation of Man and all other living things. When the Bible explained that the world was created in six days, they accepted this as an exact description of history. When the Bible explained that the world was created about 4000 years before Christ, about 6000 years before Darwin was born, they accepted this as an exact description of history.

One particular part of the Bible is important in the story of Darwin and Evolution. It explains how God spoke to Noah, a good man, and told him that the world had become a bad place, that many men were cruel and evil. To save the world, God planned to send a flood to cover the earth, and kill all the evil people. It was important to save the good people, of course, and so God told Noah to build a large boat for him and his family. As well as the people, Noah was told to take

* See *Glossary*. New words are asterisked (*) the first time they occur only.

two animals, one male and one female, from every type of animal, bird, insect etc., that lived on the earth. So that, after the flood, they could produce more animals to live on the earth.

The important point of this story is that many people believed that the men and animals living on the earth were directly descended from* the men, women and animals that came out of Noah's boat after the flood, and, also, that they were exactly the same in form, size, type and quality. In the 19th century, then, all the living things were exactly the same as God had made them, as they had come out of Noah's boat. There were no new animals, and none of the types had disappeared or stopped existing. There could be no changes, because the world was perfect when God made it.

In 1809, when Darwin was born, most people believed these things. Many people still do. The story of Darwin, however, is the story of a different explanation for the existence of the forms, types and qualities of living things on the earth, a story of change and disappearance, a story of change and improvement, a story of evolution.

It is the story of Darwin's ideas. Not everyone believed or agreed with them at that time. And not everyone believes or agrees with them now. But right or wrong, they have changed the history of the world.

1
Erasmus Darwin

Erasmus Darwin was the grandfather of Charles. They never met because Erasmus died seven years before his grandson, Charles, was born. Both Charles and Erasmus, in their different times, were fascinated* by the facts of the natural world. Both of them wrote books about the evolution* of living things. There were more similarities between their ideas than there were differences, but there was at least one important difference. It was this difference which made Charles famous and changed the thinking of the world.

In his way, Erasmus was also famous. He had written several books and there was one book written about him which was simply called *Erasmus Darwin*. The book was originally written in German and the English edition* appeared during his grandson's lifetime; it was Charles who wrote the Introduction. Erasmus was elected a member of the Royal Society. He earned his living as a doctor, and was even offered the job of Doctor to King George III – but Erasmus refused.

The three books by Erasmus, for which he is now remembered, were called *Zoonomia*, *The Temple* of

Nature, and *The Botanic* Garden*. The last two of these were written as long poems, which was not unusual in the eighteenth century. The books of Erasmus were translated into both French and German and his reputation as a writer was as great as his reputation as a scientist.

Before looking at the ideas of Erasmus in his books, it would be better to look at the ideas held by the mass of people during the eighteenth and nineteenth centuries. For three or four hundred years, travellers had been coming back to Europe with stories of strange people, strange languages and strange animals. Europeans were aware of the different nature of non-European worlds. They were taught in their churches and elsewhere, that every word of the Bible was literally* true and that what they learned from the Bible applied to the whole world, whatever it was like. From this starting point, the usual group of beliefs, conscious or unconscious, was: one, that the world was only a few thousand years old; two, that man was very different from all other living creatures and had been especially created by God; three, that the creatures which came out of Noah's ark were the same as the creatures of their own time; four, that there was no reason for any animal to change its form or for a species* to become extinct*.

Most people recognised a 'chain of being' starting from the most primitive forms of life, rising up to man himself, and then progressing even further to the angels* and up to God himself. Few, however, considered the possibility of development from one form to another. An ape* may look like a man and a sheep may resemble a goat* but the changing of one into another, or a common ancestor for both was not usually open to discussion. For the chain of being to become a theory* of evolution, not only did the idea of change and development need adding, but the whole world needed a much longer history.

There had been many intelligent people, of course, who had thought more deeply about the origin and development of living things. Not surprisingly, many of those who found the literal interpretation* of Noah and the Flood difficult to accept were interested in plants, insects, birds and animals and other phenomena* of the natural world. And there were, of course, people such as farmers who were aware that careful breeding* of certain animals could have interesting results – but no one really connected this information with the evolution of living things generally.

Erasmus Darwin certainly did not accept the Bible as literally true; and he was not alone in his ideas. Many intelligent, educated Europeans of the 18th century fully accepted the idea of unlimited change from creature to creature.

It is important, then, to briefly examine the ideas of Erasmus Darwin and two other men. These, and others, prepared the way for Charles Darwin in the 19th century. Charles never felt that he owed much to previous* thinkers, even to his famous grandfather.

What Charles offered to the world was something new; it was nevertheless an addition to, and related to, many of the thoughts of those who came before him.

The first of the three men to consider is Georges Leclerc de Buffon. He was French and lived from 1707 to 1788. He was a scientist with a special interest in living things. He suspected that not all creatures were always perfectly adapted* to their surroundings; he suspected occasional* faults and problems. He noticed that the way animals and plants were distributed over the earth suggested possible change and development in their history. He spoke about the need, in theory, for the history of the world to be much longer. He saw certain similarities between animals which did not look related. He noticed differences in the form of animals belonging to the same species and he saw that life increased faster than its food supply. None of these ideas fitted very well with the literal interpretation of the Bible. Two important books of his were published* in 1749 and 1778. It is fairly certain that the writings of Buffon influenced both Erasmus Darwin and a second Frenchman, Jean Baptiste Lamarck, who lived from 1744 to 1829. Lamarck was a deep and logical* thinker. He saw all living creatures, not only as constantly* changing, but as constantly trying to change. He believed that life was spontaneously* created at the lowest levels and that all beings, during their life, actually tried to develop into higher forms. He believed that whatever change a creature made to itself during its lifetime, that change was passed on to its children. For example, if a giraffe* managed to make its neck just a little longer by always trying to reach higher, then the children of that giraffe would have longer-than-average necks. This is not true, but to a firm believer in evolution like Lamarck, it was one of the few possible answers.

So, there were actually several scientists who did not accept the fact that all life forms were unchanging, that is to say, that no development ever took place, and that all creatures were the same as they were when God created the world. Erasmus Darwin was one of these 18th century scientists. He published his *Zoonomia* in 1794 but he had been working on it for many years. His two long poems were published in 1791 and 1803. One of his most interesting comments on living things is:

'the whole is one family of one parent'

which is exactly what his grandson was going to argue years later. That sentence summarises* the evolution of all living things in their various forms from a single, probably primitive*, living being. Erasmus noticed that living things had a special relationship with the places where they lived (today this is known as the study of 'ecology*', and the whole set of relationships is 'ecosystem*'). He was fascinated, for example, by protective colouring in animals, and by how a plant spread its seeds. He suggested that creatures just like those of long ago might still be found in deep seas (he would never have seen the coelacanth*). He was aware, too, that most living things were constantly making changes to suit their environment*.

Among certain scientists, then, the idea of evolution and constant change among living things was really quite well accepted. There were others beside Buffon, Lamarck and Erasmus Darwin; these three were among the leaders in such thinking. And one of them happened to be the grandfather of Charles Darwin. Charles supplied some of the answers to their questions. Other answers were supplied by the Austrian Gregor Mendel. More information has been supplied by 20th century scientists – but there will always be more questions.

2
The early life of Charles Darwin

Charles's father, Robert, was a doctor and he planned for his own two sons, Charles and young Erasmus, to become doctors, too. There were six children in the family. Charles was the second son and the fifth child.

The family lived in Shrewsbury in a house called The Mount. Robert was a strict* but good father. He was feared just a little by his children but loved very much by them. The family situation was not made easier by the fact that Mrs Darwin, the doctor's wife, died fairly early. Charles was only nine years old at the time of her death.

Charles's mother had been Susannah Wedgwood before she married Robert. Wedgwood is a famous name in the world of *ceramics** and Susannah was a member of the family which started that famous product. Even after Susannah's death the Darwins and the Wedgwoods remained close friends; and Charles's uncle, Josiah Wedgwood, played an important part in Charles's future. The Darwins were not a religious family, in fact, one could describe them as a family of unbelievers; unbelievers with open minds. The writings of grandfather Erasmus are a nice example of this approach to life.

Robert, like Erasmus his father, was a member of the Royal Society, which means that he was a man quite highly respected by other educated men of the time. He was also respected in Shrewsbury as a doctor. He had many patients* and became very rich. Much later, when he died, he left Charles five thousand pounds a year. This was, in those days, a very large amount of money. When Charles got married he received thirteen thousand pounds from his father in order to set up his home. In addition to this, Charles received money regularly from his father. In fact, from a financial* point of view, it was never necessary for Charles to work or get a job at all. Nevertheless, Robert, like all good fathers, often complained about the way Charles spent his money and his spare time. Robert was a big man; he was six feet two inches tall and weighed three hundred and twenty eight pounds, about 150kg. He kept a close eye on all his children and cared for their education. Charles later described him as 'the kindest man I ever knew'. He was a lively personality and very interested in the smallest details of the lives of his family and his patients. As it was Robert's plan that his sons should become doctors like their father and grandfather, Charles and young Erasmus often went with their father when he visited his patients. They watched Robert at work and helped to mix the medicines.

At the age of eight Charles was sent to school in

A statue of Charles Darwin in Shrewsbury, where he lived as a child.

Shrewsbury. It was a day school, (i.e. Charles came home every day), which was run by a Mr Case. One report which we have of this school says that Charles was slower at learning than his younger sister. This tells us something about Charles; it also tells us something about Robert, whose thinking was broad enough to send his daughters to school. Not all families sent their daughters to school in those days.

After a year at Mr Case's school, Robert sent Charles to continue his education at a traditional* boarding* school known simply as Shrewsbury School. A 'boarding' school meant that the pupils lived and slept there, apart from the holidays. A large part of their learning was the grammar of Latin and Greek. Every day the pupils would have forty or fifty lines of Latin poetry to learn by heart or translate. As an occasional change from grammar, the pupils might learn a little of the history of the ancient Greeks and Romans or even a little geography*. The school would not be very different from the school attended by William Shakespeare in Stratford more than two hundred years before. This was the normal education for the sons of successful, middle-class parents. The school was organised by Dr Samuel Butler whose own grandson later became a writer. Although the school was a boarding school, Charles visited his home most evenings, partly perhaps because it was so close to the school and partly because the home itself was a happy one. Charles started at Shrewsbury School in 1818 and remained a pupil there for seven years.

A person of the twentieth century will immediately notice that the school offered no mathematics*, no English grammar or English literature and certainly no sciences. Charles's own interests, however, certainly were in these areas rather than Latin grammar. He enjoyed reading the works of Shakespeare and Byron. He was also very interested by a book called *The Natural History of Selborne* by a clergyman* called Gilbert White. It is not surprising, therefore, to learn that Charles was very fond of bird-watching and insect collecting. He was a collector of many different things – most of them concerned with natural history.

He was also interested in chemistry* – so much so that the boys at school called him 'Gas'. This interest in chemistry was shared by his brother Erasmus. Together they fixed up a sort of chemistry laboratory* in the school gardens. When Dr Butler heard about this he was extremely angry. It is interesting to note that the boys were publicly punished by the school. Chemistry was certainly not part of a boy's education.

On the whole, school was little use to Charles. In fact, he later wrote that his 'school, as a means of education, was simply a blank*'. But he was not an unhappy person. In addition to his poems, books, birds, insects, collecting and chemistry, he became totally obsessed* by shooting and hunting as he grew older. The most important dates in his diary were the beginnings of the seasons for the shooting of certain birds and animals. At one point, his father became so angry with his son's obsession* that he was forced to say: 'You care for nothing but shooting, dogs and rat-catching and you will be a disgrace* to yourself and all your family'. These are probably not the words of a strict and unpleasant father, as some books about Darwin suggest. Taken together with all the other information about Robert, they are more likely to be the words of a caring father whose patience had ended.

One of the places where Charles could enjoy good company and good shooting was the home of his uncle — Josiah Wedgwood — 'Uncle Jos' to Charles. The house was called 'Maer' and the family was a happy one. Josiah himself was a kind and understanding person; he had a daughter called Emma who became very friendly with Charles, and whom he later married — and the shooting was excellent.

This was all very well for Charles, but his father was thinking about Charles's future. In 1825 he sent Charles to the University in Edinburgh to study medicine. Erasmus, the older son, had gone there one year before, also to study medicine. So, on 22nd October of that year, Charles became a university student.

Charles lived with his brother. In some ways he was a good student and might have become a good doctor like his father. The medical school however, was as boring to Charles as the boarding school. He attended lectures* in medicine, chemistry, anatomy*, clinics* and surgery*. He found them all 'extremely dull' except for some of the lectures in chemistry.

Erasmus did not want to become a doctor either. The two brothers watched operations* performed on children. These were the days before painkillers, and it was too much for Charles, who had to leave before the end of the operation.

Charles's private interests, however, were as important as they had been in Shrewsbury. They were all somehow concerned with life, death and change.

There was an educated and well-travelled black man living in Edinburgh. A 'pleasant and intelligent man', according to Charles. Charles paid him for lessons in the preservation* of birds. He added geology* to his interests and went out with fishermen in the River Forth. From these trips he learned several methods of catching marine* animals. He complained, however, that having caught them, he had not had enough training in dissection* from the university to study them very closely. He also needed a good microscope*, which he did not have.

The shooting continued and his reading moved away from poems towards the life sciences. He read Boswell's *Life of Johnson* but most of the books he borrowed from the library were about animal study. Examples of his reading were Fleming's *Philosophy* of Zoology*, Wood's *Insects*, and Newton's *Opticks**.

Charles was aware at this time that his father was now so financially successful that he himself would be able to lead an independent life as a collector. His father might not approve, but it was nevertheless a real possibility. It may have been with this in mind that Charles gave so much of his time to his real interests. He became a member of a group called the Plinean Society and attended lectures on natural history subjects such as the classification* of creatures or studies of particular birds such as the finch*. He also gave lectures himself. He became friends with the secretary of the society and together they attended lectures by such people as John James Audubon, an American naturalist* and painter, who loved hunting as Charles did. Together they saw Walter Scott at a meeting of the Royal Society of Edinburgh. Charles also met a William McGillivray, who had published a book about the birds of Scotland.

In the holidays there was walking, shooting and climbing in North Wales. Charles returned for his second year as a medical student on 10th November, 1826. His lectures included biology*, 'the practice of physic', zoology and geology. He found the lectures on geology so boring that his interest in it was nearly killed.

One day, Charles's friend Grant, the Plinean Society secretary, talked to Charles about Lamarck and spoke about his ideas of evolution. This reminded Charles of his grandfather's book *Zoonomia*. There was not an immediate revolution in Charles's thinking but maybe the first seeds were planted.

Charles's time at Edinburgh University was not wasted – but it certainly did not fit in with his father's plans. Charles, helped by his sisters, managed to tell his father that his future was unlikely to be in medicine. Poor old Dr Darwin brought Charles away from Edinburgh and had to think again about his son's future.

By September of 1827 Charles had been accepted as a student at the University of Cambridge. The purpose of the plan this time was for Charles to study for a suitable degree and become a clergyman. It may seem a strange decision for Dr Darwin to have made; the Darwins were not a particularly religious family, and Charles had never shown the slightest interest in those studies which were supposed to interest clergymen: Latin, Greek and the church, for example. There was one area of study, however, that was considered a perfectly acceptable, even normal, part of a country clergyman's life – natural history. If Charles became a clergyman, no one would be surprised to learn that he collected insects and other such things. The book that Charles had enjoyed at school *The Natural History of Selborne* had been written by a clergyman. Perhaps Dr Darwin's decision was not so strange after all.

Charles could not start at Cambridge immediately. He had forgotten so much, or never learned it, that he had to study in Shrewsbury with a private teacher. He did not begin to attend lectures at Cambridge until January 1828. Then he took classes in Latin and Greek, mathematics and religion. If Charles had been born in the twentieth century, he would probably not have got a university place at all. He didn't seem to mind his studies too much, although he didn't take them too seriously. At first he was a little worried about blindly accepting certain of the church ideas but perhaps he did not want to disappoint his father a second time. Cambridge offered so much riding and shooting that studies and church took second place anyway. Charles led a wonderful life filled with songs, dinners, friends, horses and dogs — and he never stopped collecting beetles*. On one occasion he was so obsessed with catching one beetle, while he was holding two others, that he put one beetle in his mouth to free his hands. He studied hard enough however, to get an ordinary degree in 1831. His father must have been relieved – but the relief would not last long.

One of the books which Charles had to read as part of his studies was *Evidences* of Christianity* by William Paley. This book considered many of the natural phenomena of the world, and gathered them together to form some very well-argued support for a literal interpretation of the creation of the world as told in the Bible. Charles much admired Paley's discussions in the book. Paley's point of view would be the one held and supported by all respectable clergymen. In his spare time Charles read Alexander von Humboldt's book about his travels in the Americas. The idea of scientific exploration seemed wonderful to Charles. He was especially excited by Humboldt's description of Tenerife. He became determined to visit that place and started to learn Spanish for that purpose.

Charles became friends with two of the teachers at the university. John Henslow who taught Botany and Adam Sedgwick who taught Geology. Charles's interest in geology grew as it had never grown before, and it never died. Charles and Adam spent some time in Wales studying the rocks and their forms. On this excursion Charles found a tropical* shell amongst the stones. Adam said that the shell must have arrived there by accident, otherwise most of the theories of geology could not be true. Charles, for the moment accepted Adam's word, but another seed had been planted in his mind. It would not grow for some time.

Far more important than geology, however, was the opening of the bird shooting season. Charles left Wales and set off for Uncle Josiah's for the sport. On the way he visited his own family at The Mount. There was a letter for him at home. It was from John Henslow. Henslow wrote that he knew a sea captain who was willing to share his cabin with a naturalist on a voyage round the world in a ship called the *Beagle*. Henslow thought that Charles was the man to go. Charles was delighted; here was his chance for scientific exploration in the style of Humboldt. His father was disappointed; just when Charles had his degree and could settle into a profession he wanted to change again to something new. Robert refused permission for Charles to go. Charles depended totally on his father for money. They discussed the matter. Finally Robert said that if Charles could find just one man of common sense who would support Charles's plan, he would change his mind. Robert loved his son and knew him well. The man was not hard to find. Uncle Jos supported Charles. Together they left the shooting at Maer, went back to visit Robert, and Robert gave his permission for Charles to go.

So Charles had two interviews with Captain* Robert Fitzroy. Fitzroy had his doubts about Charles — for one thing Charles's nose was not the right shape.

Fitzroy believed that the shape of the face had some relationship with a man's character. But he accepted Charles as naturalist for the voyage of the *Beagle* in spite of his nose. Fitzroy was an interesting man in several other ways too.

3
The *Beagle*

A beagle* is a dog, a special kind of dog used for hunting. The *Beagle* was the name of a ship of the Royal Navy*, and was the third Royal Navy ship to have this name. She was built in 1819 at Woolwich and one of her first public appearances was when she sailed right up the River Thames, under the old London Bridge, and fired her guns when George IV was crowned as king. She was the first warship ever to sail so far up the Thames.

She was not a big ship; ninety feet long (28m) and twenty-five feet (7m) wide, and built, of course, of wood. The *Beagle* herself was considered a safe ship but the class of ships to which she belonged was not popular among seamen. This was because, in heavy seas, the water flowed across the decks of the middle part of the ship. Before the voyage with Charles Darwin, Captain Fitzroy had the decks raised by twelve inches at the forward end and eight inches at the other. This not only gave better performance in the water, but much more comfort for the people who had to work on the ship.

This was the period shortly after the end of the

The Beagle — *the ship that Darwin and Fitzroy sailed on.*

Napoleonic wars. The Spanish and Portuguese govern-
ments in South America had come to an end. That
whole continent was in a state of disorganisation, and
revolutions were frequent. The British were interested
in increasing their influence in South America and the
British Admiralty* had sent several ships to explore the
coastline and make good maps. Such maps would be
useful not only for South America itself, especially the
lesser known west coast, but also for voyages* to the
Pacific.

Between 1825 and 1837 the Admiralty organised
three such voyages to South America. The voyage of
the *Beagle*, when Charles Darwin was on board, was
the second mapmaking voyage which the *Beagle* had
made to South America. The first voyage had been
unhappy but rather interesting. Two ships had gone
out; the *Adventure* and the *Beagle*. The captain of the
Beagle had shot himself during the voyage. Robert
Fitzroy had had to take the dead captain's place for the
rest of the voyage. When the *Beagle* set out on her
second South American voyage with Darwin on board
and Fitzroy as captain in 1831, it is interesting to see
that many of the crew from the first voyage were happy
to come back to the *Beagle* and to Captain Fitzroy, the
man who had become a captain under such difficult
conditions.

The first lieutenant* on the Darwin voyage was Mr
Wickham, and he became the *Beagle*'s captain for a
third surveying* voyage to Australia. Many of the
officers and crew came back for this voyage, too. This

The people on board the Beagle in 1831

Robert Fitzroy	Captain and Surveyor
John Wickham	First Lieutenant
Bartholomew Sulivan	Lieutenant
Edward Chaffers	Master
Robert MacCormick	Doctor
George Rowlett	
Alexander Derbishire	
Peter Stewart	
John Stokes	Assistant Surveyor
Benjamin Bynoe	Assistant Doctor
Arthur Mellersh	
Philip King	
Alexander Usborne	Master's assistant
Charles Masters	
Jonathan May	Carpenter
Edward Hellyer	Clerk
Thirty-four seamen	
Six boys	
Seven marines	
One sergeant of marines	
One acting boatswain	
Captain Fitzroy's servant	
Charles Darwin	Naturalist
Sims Covington	Darwin's assistant
Augustus Earle	Map drawer
George Stebbing	Instrument maker
Richard Matthews	Missionary
Jemmy Button	Fuegian
Fuegia Basket	Fuegian
York Minster	Fuegian

was later, in 1837. Charles visited the ship before she sailed. She returned to Woolwich in 1843. Her end came in 1870 when she was sold to a shipbreakers for £525.

The main interest in the *Beagle*, however, is her second voyage which began in 1831. Her job was to make maps of the coasts of South America and certain islands, and then continue on round the world and return to Britain from the east. For this voyage she had many expensive repairs. She had returned full of holes from her last voyage and now she was repaired and improved; a solid ship with a lot of reconstruction in the best wood.

At the start of the voyage Captain Fitzroy was twenty-six years old, Charles was twenty-two, most of the officers were in their twenties and the youngest was fourteen. Altogether there were seventy-four people on board. This meant that the ship was very, very crowded. Charles shared a cabin* with the ship's captain and surveyor*. The big map table was the most important thing in the cabin. Charles was able to use one end of the table for his work. When he wanted to sleep he had to remove a drawer from its place and use the empty space for his feet.

Most of the people on board were professional sailors and the ship was mainly a happy one. A few men, however, did leave the ship when they reached South America. During the whole five-year voyage twenty-five men altogether ran away from the ship. This was a smaller number than the people who were actually made to leave, which was thirty-eight.

The *Beagle* was a navy ship with six guns and excellent supplies. There was navy discipline on board, which meant that punishment for sailors could be a number of lashes* across a man's back. A total of 611 lashes were given during the whole voyage, even though Fitzroy was not a cruel man and was respected by most of his men.

4
South America

Charles was seasick almost as soon as the *Beagle* left England. He was particularly ill as she sailed south past France and Spain, but he had to live with his seasickness for the next five years, whenever the *Beagle* was at sea.

Tenerife, in the Canary Islands, was the first stop of the voyage. Charles, full of excitement and ideas from Humboldt, and eager to set foot on tropical ground, was extremely disappointed when they were not allowed to land there because there was cholera* in the islands. He had only a few days to wait, however, before they reached the Cape Verde Islands, and he was not disappointed. He was immediately fascinated by the birds, insects and flowers which were all new to him. And this fascination was to develop into an almost magical force as the *Beagle* introduced him to the South American continent.

The job of a naturalist in those days was to collect. Geological specimens*, skins and skeletons* of birds and animals, insects and plants were all gathered and noted. Whenever there was the opportunity, the collection would be sent home to the museums and

Darwin collecting specimens.

universities. The usual method of getting a specimen was to kill the creature and send it to Britain as complete as possible.

It is impossible here to consider the many adventures, dangers, wonders and discoveries that Charles experienced during the four years that the *Beagle* spent around that continent. Charles himself wrote a very full diary, and many books have since been written about those experiences and their great influence on man's knowledge of himself.

Charles spent about three months collecting specimens in the lands around Rio de Janeiro. His own happy involvement with the natural phenomena was balanced in unhappiness at the terrible situation of the slaves* he saw every day. He saw many examples of cruelty; he saw a young boy beaten over the head by his master for bringing Charles a glass of water which was not quite clean.

For two years the *Beagle* explored the 1200 miles of Argentinian coast. Charles made many journeys inland, lived with Indians, slave-owners, soldiers, murderers and cattle-kings who were total dictators* over their enormous lands. He saw colonial* behaviour at its worst, not only slavery, but the planned destruction* of native populations. And he saw the phenomena of nature, past and present, at their most wonderful. Many of the South American countries were either recently independent or fighting their way towards political organisation. Life was violent and lawless. His journeys into Argentina were usually made in the company of gauchos* — Argentinian cowboys — who were his guides and his protectors. They lived on horseback and thought little about taking a man's life. They occasionally fought each other with knives and most had marks on their faces. Charles learned to live with them and had real respect for them. Argentina possibly represented the happiest time of his life.

Exploring an Argentinian beach with Sims Covington, his assistant, Charles discovered the skull* of a very large animal that he had never seen before. It looked a bit like a rhinoceros*. Further study of this head showed it to belong to a huge rodent*. In everything but size it was like a common South American rodent called a Capybara*. The larger, and of course extinct, animal was named a Toxodon. Charles wondered about the similarity of the two animals, and the fact that they were both South American.

On another occasion he found a bone of an extinct animal which had been as big as an elephant*. But this creature, named Megatherium, was not like an elephant. It seemed to belong to the sloth* family which were, like the capybaras, fairly common South American animals.

Charles found evidence of several large animals which puzzled him. He thought a lot about them and discussed them with Captain Fitzroy. In some cases, Charles was able to find almost complete skeletons. All the animals were extremely large, all had been extinct for thousands of years, and all appeared to be related to smaller modern animals living on the same land.

There was a connection between these animal discoveries and the evidence of geology. Some explanation is needed at this point. Among the books Charles had taken with him on the voyage was one by Charles Lyell called *Principles* of Geology*. The facts and research* in this book were greatly respected by most learned men of the time, but few agreed with the actual theories which the book presented. The main idea in *Principles of Geology* was that the history of the earth was one, long, uninterrupted, gradual, ever-continuing development. The climate and other forms of movement and change were always influencing the nature of the surface of the earth. For this theory to be possible, the earth needed to be many millions of years old. This set of beliefs about the earth came to be known as 'uniformitarianism' — that is to say, the history of the earth could be told in a single long story. Most educated men of the time, including Captain Fitzroy, held a set of beliefs which can be called 'catastrophism'. In short, they believed that the history of the earth had progressed in clear and separate stages. Each stage was separated by a catastrophe* and was represented by one geological level. The last of the great catastrophes had been Noah's flood, this beginning the present stage. Most important of all, within each stage, no development was possible; all life remained unchanged until the next catastrophe. Charles's discoveries did not support catastrophism very well; they supported uniformitarianism much more easily. The catastrophist,

Captain Fitzroy, had his own explanation, described in the next chapter, but Charles wondered about that, too.

Charles's experiences, journeys, adventures and deep thinking continued as the *Beagle* turned north up the Pacific coast of the continent. Charles's father had been right after all. The young, carefree, bird-shooting clergyman had disappeared. Charles was no longer just a collector. He had changed — he knew he was a scientist: here was the beginning of Charles Darwin, the thinker.

On a long journey into the Andes*, Charles discovered marine fossils* miles from the sea. He had discovered another large extinct animal with a smaller modern relative; the larger one was the Macrauchenia and its relative the Guanaco*. He knew the Rhea well, which is the Ostrich* of South America, but he had only heard of the 'Petise', a similar related bird which was supposed to live further south than the Rhea. One evening, after just discovering that he had eaten Petise for supper, he ran to the cook to rescue the head, wings and neck as specimens. If Fitzroy and the Bible were right, why had God created two birds so similar and so close together?

Strangely, it was a catastrophe which gave Charles some help in the problems of resemblances. An earthquake* affecting four hundred miles of coast and involving the eruption* of a chain of volcanoes*, destroyed the town of Concepcion. Fitzroy and Charles visited the area. It was clear to both of them that the level of the land was not the same after the earthquake as before. Things were not unchangeable, so it was possible, over a long period of time, for the Andes to have risen out of the sea. This would explain how marine fossils were found inland.

On the island of Chiloe, a fox* came so close to Charles that he was able to hit it on the head with his geological hammer and take it as a specimen. It was related to the foxes of the mainland, but not quite the same. Why not?

Charles had always been fascinated by insects. One evening, to entertain some friends, he put an insect called a Benchuga on a table, let it take a bite from his finger and suck the blood. The group watched as the insect grew fatter and fatter with Charles's blood. It was painless to Charles. It is now known that the Benchuga carries a disease called Chagas's disease. It is quite possible, though not absolutely certain, that Charles had this disease for the rest of his life.

5
Robert Fitzroy

Charles was liked by everyone he met — from South American gauchos to Captain Fitzroy himself. Captain Fitzroy was not the sort of person that many people liked — he was the sort of person that people admired and respected. Fitzroy was no ordinary man.

He was an aristocrat*, descended from Charles II. Although born into the top social level, his early life had not been easy — certainly not as carefree* as Charles's own early life.

He was born in Suffolk in 1805, and twelve years later went to the Royal Navy College in Portsmouth. His progress at the college was very distinguished. He was made lieutenant when he was nineteen years old, after sailing in the Mediterranean, the Channel and to South America.

When Captain Stokes killed himself on the *Beagle* during the ship's first South American surveying voyage, Fitzroy was given command of the *Beagle* on the order of the Admiralty.

On that same voyage, the people of Tierra del Fuego had stolen a small boat from the *Beagle*. In return, Fitzroy took four Fuegian prisoners. The Fuegians preferred the small boat, and Fitzroy therefore kept his prisoners.

Fitzroy was a strong believer in the universal good of Christianity. He brought the four Fuegians to England where one of them died. He paid for the others to be educated. They became well-known and were invited to visit the Queen. Fitzroy's intention was to return them to their homeland where they would help to 'civilise' the other Fuegians. When it seemed that Fitzroy's job would not take him to Tierra del Fuego, he prepared to send a ship to take the men back. He would pay for it himself. However, at the last moment he was given command of the *Beagle* again, with special instructions to survey the southern tip of South America and so the three Fuegians sailed with him. Unfortunately this experiment with the Fuegians was a complete failure. At first the three men, called Fuegia Basket, York Minster and Jemmy Button could not communicate with their own countrymen when they returned to Tierra del Fuego. Jemmy Button even tried to speak English to them, and then asked them in Spanish why they did not understand him. Ten days after their re-introduction, Matthews, the missionary* who had planned to stay in the country and convert them to Christianity was rescued by Fitzroy. He had no food, no belongings and no where to live. One year later, the three Fuegians were no different from their countrymen. Fitzroy was disappointed, but Charles was not surprised.

Fitzroy was a distinguished seaman and an excellent

surveyor. Discipline was hard on his ship but he was respected by his men. All ships's captains were very powerful people when the ship was at sea, but Fitzroy was never a blind dictator.

Although he did not like the shape of Charles's nose when he interviewed him for the job of naturalist on the voyage, Fitzroy liked his open manner, and Charles soon developed a great admiration for Fitzroy. They remained friends for many years after the voyage in spite of the ever-growing distance between their beliefs.

On the voyage, Fitzroy wanted Charles to discover as much evidence as possible in support of the word-for-word belief in the Bible which he, and many other educated people, held. He hoped, for example, that Charles would find evidence of Noah's flood. Fitzroy was never more wrong in his choice of man, but of course it was never, at any time, Charles's own intention to throw doubt upon the Bible. The evidence that he found simply did not agree with the age of the world according to the Bible, or a literal interpretation of the Noah's ark story.

When Charles discussed with Fitzroy the giants of the Argentinian beaches, Megetherum, Macrauchenia etc., Fitzroy suggested that these animals had simply failed to get into Noah's ark, had been left behind, and so left no descendants*. When Charles looked around at the sloths and guanacos, he was not so sure that they had left no descendants. But Fitzroy had a terrible temper, and Charles learned to be careful about disagreeing with him. When Charles, for example, had said how terrible he felt about the situation of the slaves in Brazil, Fitzroy was so angry with Charles because he disagreed with him that he asked him to leave his cabin.

Fitzroy believed in the literal truth of the Bible, and that there was nothing better than Christianity; he was not capable of open discussion on these matters. Somewhere in Fitzroy's beliefs there seemed to be a weakness, though Fitzroy would never discover it. Indeed, the older he grew, the more firmly fixed he became in his beliefs.

An extremely brave and hard-working man, Fitzroy was a product of the orthodox* education and religion of those times. Most educated people shared his views. Charles would later explode the basis* for many of Fitzroy's beliefs, and it was on Fitzroy's ship that Charles prepared this. But Fitzroy himself was never to change. He was a man of his times and, in his way, a great contributor* to the progress of those times.

In 1865, when he was 59, he killed himself by cutting his throat. The reason is not known.

6
The Galapagos Islands

After nearly four years around South America, three or four weeks in the Galapagos Islands did not seem like a very important part of the voyage. South America had been especially important in Captain Fitzroy's surveying plans, and Charles had seen many wonderful and thought-disturbing things on that continent. No one expected anything really special from this group of volcanic islands hundreds of miles out into the Pacific, off the coast of Ecuador. The islands were not on regular shipping voyages, and not especially beautiful.

Indeed, nothing very special did happen to the men of the *Beagle* during their stay there. It was only afterwards, on the voyage across the Pacific, and for many years back in England, that the importance of the Galapagos Islands' biology grew and grew in Charles's mind until it became the socially unwelcome, revolutionary idea that he is now famous for. It was the evidence of the Galapagos Islands that finally helped to persuade Charles that man is a part of nature, and not apart from it. Most Europeans found this idea rather uncomfortable.

There were birds, insects and reptiles* on the is-

lands, but no mammals*. The most well-known animals were the giant tortoises* which lived in thousands
on the islands. These reptiles were big enough to carry
a man easily on their backs, and it needed at least four
men to lift one. The name 'Galapagos' is actually the
Spanish word for these tortoises. Seamen knew of them
as a form of food. Some ships had taken up to eight
hundred of them on board to use as fresh meat. In 1835,
when Charles visited the islands, the destruction of the
tortoises by man — for profit and for meat — had
already begun, but there were still plenty.

Today there are only about six thousand of them in
the whole of the islands. Four of the fifteen kinds have
become extinct and two more kinds are almost extinct.

Charles learned that the variety of tortoises on one
island was slightly different from the variety of tortoises on another. He talked to a government official
who could name the original island of a tortoise simply
by looking at the tortoise's shape. This was interesting,
but did not seem very significant* to Charles. It was
one of those seeds which was to develop in his mind; it
needed time to grow.

Charles found twenty-five new kinds of bird, fifteen
new kinds of fish, sixteen new land shells, a few new
beetles out of the twenty-five species he collected, and
a hundred new plants out of the hundred and eighty he
collected. It was clear that the new finds existed only in
the Galapagos Islands, but equally clear that they were
all closely related to forms of life in South America.
They were not South American but they suggested

South America. This was another of those ideas planted in Charles's mind which he simply kept and thought about.

He recognised thirteen species of bird which all belonged to the finch family. As with the tortoises, he only later realised the importance of noting which species came from which island. When he was sorting his specimens on board the *Beagle* after leaving the islands, he realised what a serious mistake he had made by not organising them according to their island of origin.

He noticed that some iguanas* never moved more than ten metres from the sea, could swim well and eat under water, but never went into the sea more than was absolutely necessary. He noticed that other iguanas lived entirely on land, ate plants and lived in holes in the ground. He noticed, almost as soon as he arrived there, that the birds were completely unafraid of man, even though sailors had been killing them for hundreds of years.

The doubts and thoughts born in South America began — and only began — to form into a theory in Charles's mind. If Captain Fitzroy and educated Europe were right, then God had created all these creatures especially for the Galapagos Islands — to live there and nowhere else. And why had God made them so closely related to the animals in South America? Another possibility was that the ancestors of the Galapagos animals had come from South America to the Galapagos Islands, and had gradually evolved —

changed — into the special creatures of the Galapagos Islands.

But — said Fitzroy and educated Europe — animals cannot change. There is no development. They are now, exactly as their ancestors were, when they came out of Noah's ark.

It had never been Charles's intention to bring home revolutionary ideas from the voyage of the *Beagle*, but he had been collecting evidence for four years now. And the total of that evidence supported the idea of change and evolution. The idea had, after all, been suggested by grandfather Erasmus. But Charles began to think about how animals managed to change, and why they changed. Part of the answer to these questions was Charles's own great contribution* to science — the theory of natural selection*, or the survival* of the creatures best suited to their environment. He never did discover exactly how one animal could be slightly different from its parents.

The Galapagos Islands are about six hundred miles away from South America. They are also separated from each other by deep water, and there is not much wind in this part of the world to carry seeds or small creatures between the islands. They presented to Charles a perfect example of evolution at work. Charles later realised that the thirteen finches represented thirteen different ways in which the (probable) single parent-species had adapted to life in the islands. The fifteen varieties of tortoise were another beautifully clear example of the same kind of development.

If the *Beagle* had visited the Galapagos Islands early in the voyage, their significance would almost certainly have been lost on Charles, the carefree collector. As it was, their geographical position almost exactly matched the readiness in Charles's mind for their evidence. (We must say 'almost' matched, because Charles failed to organise his finches according to each island.)

In the same way that the seeds and animals of South America had created new life in the Galapagos Islands, so the islands themselves planted seeds in Charles's mind, which he, in turn, took away to create new life in man's thinking.

7
Down House

The voyage of the *Beagle* lasted for about five years. That voyage was probably the most significant group of events in Charles's whole life. His whole life, however, lasted for seventy-three years, and for forty of those seventy-three years Charles lived in the same house in the village of Downe in Kent. In those days the name of the village was spelt 'Down' but the twentieth-century villagers prefer the name with an 'e' on the end. There is no difference in pronunciation.

Down was less than twenty miles (32 km) from London, but very much in the country — quiet and peaceful. The forty years that Charles lived there were the last forty of his life and amounted to over half of his lifetime.

Down House itself was a big house with eighteen acres* (ca 80,000 sq.m.) of land, with gardens, and fruit trees, in quiet country. Today it can be visited by the public and Charles's study can be seen in a condition not very different from when he worked there for forty years. The quietness, gentleness, and regularity of life at Down House could not have been more different

Down House in Kent where Darwin lived for much of his life.

from the voyage of the *Beagle* and the adventures around the world.

From the Galapagos Islands, the *Beagle* sailed west, across the Pacific, visited the Society Islands, New Zealand, Australia, the Keeling Islands in the Indian Ocean, Mauritius, South Africa, into the Atlantic once again to call at St Helena and Ascension Island. At Ascension Island it seemed as if Europe was almost in sight. But Captain Fitzroy kept the *Beagle* pointing to the west until the ship once more arrived at the east coast of South America. It was very important for Fitzroy's measurements that the ship did a complete circuit of the Earth before returning to England. It was for this reason that the *Beagle* had to touch South America for a second time. The 360-degree journey completed and the measurements made, the *Beagle* really did head for home. The ship arrived at Falmouth in Cornwall on 2nd October 1836.

Charles hurried to see his family and Uncle Jos's family as soon as possible. Charles the carefree, cheerful, shooting man had left them five years earlier. Charles the scientist, still cheerful but certainly different, had come home. His father said that even the shape of Charles's head had changed.

The letters and specimens that Charles had been sending to England during the past five years had already made his reputation. He was already something of a famous man at the time of his arrival. After some time with his family and friends Charles started to live in Great Marlborough Street, London. With the help of other scientists, he began to organise his specimens. He had special responsibility for the geological specimens. Geology was still Charles's main area of professional interest. His interest in the ability of species to change their form was still there and gradually becoming larger. But Charles did not know what was in the future. The origin of species was just one of many ideas in Charles's mind.

One day, two years after coming home, Charles was reading 'for fun' a book about human population by the clergyman and economist, Malthus. The main idea in the book was that at any time, more people are born than are needed for a population to remain the same size. Two more ideas came from this, first that something was needed to control the growth of population, for example, wars, diseases, too little food, etc. and secondly that a population could grow rapidly if conditions were favourable. The idea of natural selection hit Charles like a flash of lightning. He had now realised the *how* of evolution. Evolution was not a new idea, but evolution by natural selection was. Only the fittest, only the members of the species best adapted to the environment, survived. If the environment changed then different members of the species might survive better. This was an idea of some significance – but for the moment Charles kept it to himself and was just glad that he had found a solution to a long-standing problem.

One of the other ideas in his mind was marriage. After thinking it over in his usual logical and scientific way, Charles decided that marriage would be a good thing for him. He married Emma Wedgwood, Uncle Jos's daughter, in January 1839. Earlier the same month he had moved to Upper Gower Street in London, which seemed a better place for a married couple to live.

Charles lived an extremely busy life. In the same year that he got married he wrote the *Journal of Researches* which was his own story of the voyage of the *Beagle*. Even today it makes an interesting travel book. What pleased Charles was that his hero, Humboldt, liked the book very much. He was still busy with his specimens at the Geological Society. By December of the same year, the first child — William Erasmus — was born. The second child — Anne Elizabeth — was born fifteen months later. At Upper Gower Street Charles wrote an outline of some ideas on the origin* of species, and his second book, which was a geological book.

Down House cost two thousand two hundred pounds in 1842. Charles's father paid for it. Charles and Emma moved in on 17th September and on 23rd September the third child was born. This was a girl called Mary Eleanor — but she lived for only three weeks. Almost exactly a year later another girl was born, Henrietta Emma. Charles and Emma had ten children altogether. After these four, the others were: George Howard born in 1845, Elizabeth in 1847, Francis in 1848, Leonard in 1850 and Horace in 1851. Only one month before Horace was born, ten-year-old Anne Elizabeth died. The last child was a son, Charles Waring, born at the end of 1856 when Charles himself was forty-seven years old.

Charles at the age of forty-seven, twenty years after the arrival of the *Beagle* at Falmouth, father of nine living children, author of many published works on biology and geology, was in pain for some part of every day of the forty years he lived at Down House. Perhaps it was Chagas's Disease — it is not known. Certainly, he was never able to work for more than an hour or two each day. He took a great interest in his own health but was still basically a happy man, loved by his wife and children and loving them in turn. In this same year, 1856, Charles at last began work on a very long book about species and their origin. The work contained all his ideas on evolution by natural selection etc. and a huge amount of evidence in support of those ideas. The evidence came not only from the voyage of the *Beagle* but from twenty years more observation and experiments with birds, worms, plants and many other forms of life. Charles worked on this book for two and a half years and would have continued for many more, but 1858 was a sad and significant year for Charles. Sad because his youngest son, Charles Waring, died, aged two and a half years, and significant because Charles received a letter from a man called Wallace who was working in the Far East.

8
Alfred Wallace

In 1858, when Charles received the significant letter from Wallace, it was sixteen years since he had moved into Down House, twenty years since he had discovered the principle of evolution by natural selection, and two years since he had begun writing his 'big book' on species. The 'big book' was Charles's own name for this work. Many people have suggested reasons why Charles waited eighteen years before putting his ideas of natural selection into a book. Was it because he saw in advance the storm it would cause? Was it because even his friends were not quite prepared to accept it totally? Was it to protect the more orthodox opinions of his wife? No one knows.

Whatever the reason, he finally started writing in 1856. He may never have finished the work, for it was certainly going to be very long.

After waiting eighteen years to start it, and after working on it for only two years, he was forced to change his plan from the day he received Wallace's letter. He was just beginning to write the eleventh chapter*, which was about birds, when the letter arrived.

Alfred Russel Wallace was an Englishman, fourteen years younger than Charles. He was a naturalist and a collector who had been writing to Charles for some years. He had travelled in the Amazon and was now living in the Mollucas in the Far East. Like Charles, he knew that the idea of evolution of species was unavoidable. He and Charles had exchanged letters about species but he had never mentioned natural selection. This was no surprise since Charles was the discoverer of the idea and had kept it to himself for twenty years. Wallace had published some of his writings about species and knew as much about the subject as Charles.

Wallace, too, had read Malthus on population and he, too, had thought about connections between man and all other living species. He, too, accepted the idea of evolution without much difficulty and he, too, spent much time wondering about the method of evolution; about *how* one species evolved from another. The solution came to Wallace as suddenly as it had come to Charles. Wallace was not reading Malthus at the time, as Charles had been. Wallace had already read Malthus. When Wallace saw the light he was lying ill in a hospital bed: natural selection! selection by natural methods of the fittest to survive*! the survival of those best suited to their environment! It did not matter how you said it, there was the solution. Wallace was quite excited. He thought it all out in hospital and then spent two days writing it all down. The title he gave to his paper was 'On the Tendencies* of Varieties to Depart from the Original Type'. Who would be most interested in reading it, he wondered. Charles Darwin in England, of course. He sent the paper to Charles with a short letter. The letter asked Charles to read the paper and send it to Charles Lyell, the great geologist, if Charles thought the paper had any value.

Charles had two particularly close friends at this time. It happened that one of them was Charles Lyell himself, and the other one was Joseph Hooker, who had been a naturalist on a voyage to the Antarctic.

Wallace's paper contained a short but very clear explanation of the idea of evolution by natural selection. Wallace had reached exactly the same idea as Charles Darwin. He even used some of the same words as Charles, to explain the idea. Wallace's letter was like a bomb to Charles. Charles had waited eighteen years before starting to write, and was writing a book which was so long that it would take several more years to complete. Many times his friends Lyell and Hooker had tried to persuade Charles to publish his ideas. And now Wallace had written the first clear explanation of natural selection.

Scientists are often secret and jealous about their work. It is very important to them to be known as the *first* to publish a new idea or a new discovery. Charles must have felt the wish to do nothing about Wallace's letter and then quickly publish his own ideas. After all, he was the first and real discoverer of the theory of natural selection. Charles did not do anything like that. He sent Wallace's letter to Lyell, as Wallace had asked. Charles, Lyell and Hooker needed to talk, very soon.

The result was a very fair one. At a meeting of the Linnean Society just one month later, two papers were read out for the members. One was Wallace's paper and the other contained Charles's own explanation of the theory. These papers were the introduction to the world of the idea of evolution by natural selection. The members listened politely. No one was disturbed. There was no storm. Months later, when the secretary of the Linnean Society was writing his report for the year 1858, he said that during the year there had been no great revolutionary discoveries in science. He had heard, but not understood.

Wallace's paper was only about twelve pages long. The idea was clearly explained but there was no evidence, and there were no facts to support that idea. The case with Charles was totally different. He had been collecting evidence for twenty-five years, and organising that evidence for about twenty of them. He had masses of facts and examples to support his big book on that subject. He needed to write a shorter book on the same subject, which could be in the shops soon. He reduced the plan of his big book and, thirteen months later, produced the shorter one. It was called *On the Origin of Species by Means of Natural Selection, or the Preservation of Favoured Races in the Struggle for Life*. Even this title was shorter than the one Charles had wanted. The book became known simply as *The Origin of Species* and was one of the most famous books in science and in the English language.

As far as the history of science is concerned, it seems

unfair to say that Wallace's most important contribution was making Charles hurry up. Wallace continued to send letters to Charles and sometimes had ideas which were clearer, more original and more advanced than Charles's own. He had no hesitation in saying, in 1864, that man himself was not a special creation and was no exception to the laws of evolution. Man is what he is because of natural selection, said Wallace. That was a brave thing to say in 1864. He lived for thirty-one more years after Charles had died. He and Hooker were two of the people who carried Charles's body into Westminster Abbey when he died.

9
The Origin of Species

Charles Darwin wrote about a dozen books on different details of the evolution of species, and other books
on related subjects. *The Origin of Species* is the most
famous of all Charles Darwin's books. It is one of the
most important books in the history of evolutionary
biology. More than that; it is a book which caused man
to reconsider his own place in the universe. It is not,
however, a book of philosophy; it is a book full of
fairly obvious and well-argued opinions taken from
thousands of facts, experiences, experiments and
observations.

The full title of the book is given in the previous
chapter. It is now generally known simply as *The
Origin of Species*. The word 'evolution' is not used
much in the book; Charles used the word more in *The
Descent of Man* twelve years later.

Charles always considered *The Origin of Species* as
his 'little book' because it was a shorter form of his 'big
book' which was never published — at least in the form
which Charles had planned. The title of the big work
was going to be *Natural Selection* and it was going to be
several separate books. *Natural Selection* is not lost to

the world; the contents are spread through Charles's other books.

There is no doubt that the 'little book', the famous *Origin of Species*, was the direct result of Wallace's letter to Charles, and pressure from Charles's friends to end his twenty-year delay in publishing his ideas.

The publisher of the book was John Murray. Even after all the arrangements had been made, there were still signs of hesitation and doubt from Charles. Charles still seemed to be looking for a way of escape when he wrote to John Murray. In his letter Charles said that he would be quite happy to break off the arrangements if John Murray wanted to.

John Murray did not want to break off anything. *The Origin of Species* was published on the 24th November 1859. The price of the book was fifteen shillings* and there were twelve hundred and fifty copies in the first edition. Every one of the twelve hundred and fifty copies was sold on the first day. Three thousand more copies (i.e. the second edition) were published six weeks later. The third edition of two thousand copies appeared one year later. By 1866, five years after the third edition, a fourth edition of twelve hundred and fifty copies was necessary, as well as a fifth edition of another two thousand copies in 1869. After the fifth edition of *The Origin of Species*, Charles published *The Descent of Man* (seven and a half thousand copies). The result of this was a sixth edition of *The Origin of Species* in 1872 — another three thousand copies.

Since Charles's death there have been many editions of *The Origin of Species*. The latest edition was in 1979, with notes by Richard Leakey and called *The Illustrated Origin of Species*.

In 1859, when the first edition was published, it contained a great number and variety of facts in support of natural selection. Charles discussed specialised improvement, adaptation, extinction, change and non-change in species. He suggested the possibility of a human population explosion, and made several other suggestions about the origin of life which still stand today. But why was everyone so interested? In simple words, because people thought it was a book about man, because it seemed to go against the truth of the Bible and, most of all, because it seemed to suggest that man was not a special creation by God, but just one of the more successful animals. In other words, man no longer looked up to the angels as his relatives, but down past the apes to the lowest forms of life. Until the 24th November 1859 it was still possible to accept some idea of man's evolution without throwing away the idea of man as a special creation of God. Natural selection reduced man to a successful ape. The idea of natural selection threw out God's help.

The only words in the book which actually mention man are: 'light will be thrown on the origin of man and his history'. Only a dozen words, but enough to cause a storm. Charles must have realised the effect his ideas would have. He had delayed publishing them for twenty years and was hesitant up to the last moment.

He himself had prepared to be a clergyman.

'How extremely stupid not to have thought of that,' said T H Huxley, the zoologist and friend of Charles, when he first read the book. The book was reviewed* in *The Times* newspaper. The usual scientific reviewer was ill. Huxley was asked to write the review: Charles and his little book gained a powerful supporter. Two of the enemies they gained were Charles's old friend at Cambridge, Adam Sedgwick, and the anatomist Richard Owen. Owen, already famous and respected, became the book's bitterest enemy. He wrote many nameless attacks and gave his support to every kind of attack from other people, although he and Charles had once been friends.

For months people talked about natural selection — many of them as if it were shocking. The first real public discussion of the book happened about six months after the first edition. There was a conference in Oxford organised by the British Association. There were several meetings but at one of them a very well-known bishop* planned to express his views on natural selection. To the public he was known as Soapy Sam; the bishop's real name was Samuel Wilberforce. He was a clever speaker and an enemy of Charles. Large crowds came to the meeting, and Robert Fitzroy was there. At the last moment T H Huxley was persuaded to speak against Soapy Sam, and in support of Charles Darwin. Bishop Wilberforce gave a clever and entertaining speech. The great moment of his speech was when he turned to Huxley and said:

'Is it through your grandfather or your grandmother that you are descended from a monkey*?'

The audience loved it. Huxley made no immediate
reply. Soapy Sam felt that he had victory in his hands,
and completed his speech. Huxley stood up and began
his own speech. Some of the audience were not paying
much attention. How could Huxley fight the powerful
and popular bishop? Huxley said something like this:

> 'If I had an ape for a grandfather, would it change
> my present morality and responsibilities? I tell
> you this; if I had to choose for a grandfather either
> an ape or an educated bishop who uses his clever
> words to bring ridicule* into a scientific discus-
> sion — then I would prefer to have an ape for a
> grandfather.'

There was loud laughter in the meeting. One lady
fainted and was carried out. Robert Fitzroy, less adapt-
able than ever, stood up and held the Bible over his
head, shouting 'The Book, the Book'. The chairman of
the meeting, Charles's old friend Henslow, had difficulty in keeping order.

Most of the enemies remained enemies and continued to attack the idea of evolution by natural selection, in the belief that they were supporting God. Such
people still exist today.

The Origin of Species was soon translated into other
languages, and the same arguments broke out in other

countries. The third German edition of the book was bought by a man called Gregor Mendel, who lived in what is now Czechoslovakia but was then part of Austria. He studied the book quite a lot and made marks on certain pages.

10
Gregor Mendel

After he had left Edinburgh in 1827 and before he went to Cambridge, Charles went on a short visit to Paris with Uncle Jos. This was his only experience of Europe. Places like Austria or Hungary were more foreign to him than tropical forests and volcanic islands.

Gregor Mendel lived in just such a place; far from the sea, in a land then called Moravia, now a part of Czechoslovakia. His family was poorer than Charles's. When Gregor Mendel had a chance to enter the church as a profession, it was not only the chance of a job, but his only chance for a real education. He could not be as free to choose as Charles. He entered the church as a young man and remained in it for the rest of his life, as a teacher, and a clergyman. He never travelled widely but his mind was as open as that of any man of his time.

He was born in 1822, thirteen years after Charles. When he started his own experiments, at the age of thirty-five, he had never heard of Charles. He never met Charles at any time but later on his bookshelves were Erasmus's *Zoonomia* as well as *The Origin of*

Species, along with many other books on similar subjects.

In this short story of Charles Darwin, Gregor Mendel is only interesting because he spent most of his life working on — and finding the solution to — one particular problem. And if Charles had studied Gregor's work, Charles would have had the solution to the greatest difficulty in his own work. By the time Charles died, in 1882, Gregor Mendel's book had been available for about sixteen years. Unfortunately, the success of *The Origin of Species* was not repeated with Gregor's work. Gregor's book remained unknown and without influence until many years after both Charles and Gregor were dead.

The problem which worried Charles and fascinated Gregor was inheritance*; that is to say, how and why the offspring* (i.e. children) of any form of life (plants, insects, people, etc.) look like, and behave like, their parents. What exactly is it that is passed from parents to children? The main differences between Charles and Gregor in their approach to this problem was that Charles desperately wanted to know how a child could be slightly different from its parents, and Gregor wanted to know why a child is almost the same as its parents. Really they were struggling with the same problem. As it happened, Gregor's methods produced the solution; Charles's did not.

Both men made many experiments in breeding. Charles used birds and some flowers. Gregor had a much more specialised approach. He worked mainly with sweet pea plants and studied the subject much more deeply. He bred many thousands of plants and studied the offspring for many generations*.

Charles wrote a book about inheritance. It had one of his typically long titles: *Variation of Animals and Plants under Domestication**. The book represented a very advanced viewpoint for the time. Charles's book was based upon two ideas which are now known to be false, but which were the best at that time.

The first of these ideas was mentioned in Chapter One of this story. It was the idea that a characteristic* gained by a creature during its lifetime, for example, a man's strong hands, could be passed on to the offspring. This is called the inheritance of acquired* characteristics. It is an idea now mainly connected with the name of Jean Baptiste Lamarck, accepted by Charles and now thought to be wrong.

The second false basis of Charles's book was the theory of 'blending* inheritance'. This simply means that any child is a simple mixture of its mother and father. Here is a very simple explanation of this false theory of inheritance: if one parent is a tin of white paint and the other parent is a tin of red paint, then the two mixed together produce a tin of pink paint. So, red father and white mother produce a pink child. If the second generation is pink, then future generations will also be pink. Red will disappear and white will disappear. This is what worried Charles; the theory of blending inheritance did not encourage new species and new forms. And Charles's whole theory of evolution by natural selection was based upon the idea of new species and new forms. Natural selection, helped by the environment, was a part of the answer — but not all of it. Charles knew there was a weakness somewhere, but he never found it.

What Gregor Mendel discovered, through his thousands of experiments with pea plants, was the theory of 'particulate inheritance'. Instead of two tins of paint as the example, take two tins of sand. One of red sand and one of white sand. If these are mixed together, the offspring may look like pink sand, but the individual bits of red sand and white sand never disappear. In future generations, millions of combinations of red sand grains and white sand grains are possible. Red never disappears; white never disappears. In very simple terms, this was Gregor's contribution.

Charles never used paint and Gregor never used sand in their experiments. They were, of course, concerned with living things.

Here is another simple example of Gregor's experiments. Gregor took, as the parents, one pea plant with smooth peas and one pea plant with rough peas. The 'children' of the first generation were all smooth, there was no mixing of the two characteristics. But Mendel knew that the parent round peas had round peas as their own parents, but that the new round peas came from round and rough parents. They looked the same but there was a difference in their inheritance. Next, Gregor took the new round peas as parents. For every four of their children there were three round peas for every one rough pea, or 75% round and 25% rough. One or the other; never a mixture of the two.

In his own experiments Charles came extremely near to discovering this three-to-one system, but he never fully realised its significance. The particulate inheritance of Gregor led to never-ending variety. The blending inheritance of Charles (and the rest of the world) led to ever more sameness.

As Charles's friends had persuaded him to read a paper on his ideas to the Linnean Society in London, so Gregor's friends persuaded Gregor to read his paper to the Natural History Society of Brünn. The result with both audiences was similar — polite misunderstanding. Charles published the same ideas in a book and became famous throughout the world. Gregor published his ideas in a book and this book remained unknown. Charles was one of the millions of people who never read it.

By the time that Charles was writing *The Descent of Man*, about 1870, he knew that Natural Selection was not the complete answer to the evolution of new species, but he was still rightly sure that new species evolved from old species. Even Gregor did not really believe that new species evolved in this way — he was, after all, a man of the church.

The answer to Charles's problem lay on a bookshelf in Austria perhaps next to the third German edition of *The Origin of Species*. The development of Gregor's theory had to wait until the twentieth century.

11
Extinction

Many everyday ideas of the twentieth century were revolutionary ideas when they were suggested by *The Origin of Species*. Of all the new ideas, the idea of extinction was one of the most difficult for people to understand. In the confident Christianity of nineteenth-century Europe, it seemed impossible that a whole species of animal could disappear from the surface of the earth. The idea was simply too new. Not only would it make the story of Noah's Ark (and therefore, the Bible) seem wrong, but it would suggest that God had done something wrong when he created all the animals. Surely God's creations could not die out. People could think of no reason why a species should disappear; if God had created it, then it would be there for ever. If species could become extinct, then the whole world would not be the wonderful safe place that many people thought it was, where man was master of everything. If man was just a successful ape, then any other species might have been just as successful and man might have disappeared, too. That was a truly impossible thought for them. Impossible for them because they believed that man was different.

A dinosaur.

They believed that man was closer to God than to the apes, and was not a part of nature like other creatures. Even if Charles was right about the animals, he couldn't expect 'educated' people to believe that they had cousins in the trees. It is easy to understand why that lady fainted at the Oxford meeting when T H Huxley said that he would rather be related to an ape than to a bishop. That was an amazing thing to say in those days.

It took society as a whole a long time to accept the idea of extinction because it meant throwing out so many other ideas — ideas that were very important to people in those times. It was difficult enough for them to accept the idea that the earth was hundreds of millions of years old. It was even more difficult for them to accept that the bones which Charles found in South America belonged to creatures which had already died out millions of years ago.

Even today many people find it difficult to understand the absolute finality of extinction. Not long ago there was a young schoolboy in America who had to choose an animal to study for his school work. He didn't want a well-known ordinary animal, so he wrote to the San Diego zoo and asked for information about 'a really extinct animal' that he could go and study. He could not understand the real meaning of extinct.

In the twentieth century, man has become aware of two kinds of extinction. First there is the slow and natural extinction of a species. This happens over a very long period, as one species loses the competition against a more advanced species, or, as it fails to change when its environment changes. In this way, new species slowly develop and take the place of the old species. Some people think this is why the dinosaurs* disappeared. The other kind of extinction is less natural and much more rapid. During Charles's own lifetime, for example, there were millions of wild bison* in North America. Just over one hundred years later they have disappeared, because of hunting and the settling of the land. If they had disappeared for reasons of evolution by natural selection, then it might have needed millions more years and nature would have provided something in their place. The unnatural rapid extinction of species has been happening every single year in the twentieth century and had begun to happen even before Charles's lifetime.

The successful ape called man now adapts the environment to his needs instead of slowly adapting himself to the environment. This sometimes results in the destruction of the home-environment of other species. These species then become extinct long before their natural time; and there is no natural replacement for them. It was not until the middle of the twentieth century that man really began to realise how much his own short-term plans were interfering with natural selection and other slower systems of the earth's ecosystem.

For the people of the nineteenth century, the world was about six thousand years old. It was a truly great contribution to make them able to look back many millions of years. At the same time, Charles Darwin seemed to separate them from God, and most of them did not like it. Many people felt Darwin was trying to show that God did not exist, or that he did not control the world. This was not Darwin's intention, but he could not make the facts he had agree with the Bible stories. Darwin's explanations became very popular, but there has always been disagreement. Many religious people refuse to accept his evidence, and in some countries, such as the United States, groups of people have tried to prevent the teaching of his ideas in schools.

There is disagreement also from other scientists, especially now in the 1980s. While accepting that evolution happens, that living things can change, some scientists disagree with the type and the speed of the changes. Darwin believed that only a slow and gradual evolution, the principle of natural selection, could explain the evidence of fossils. In the study of fossils, it is clear that many animals changed a lot over a long period of years. But scientists now believe that these changes were not slow and gradual, as Darwin said. Some believe that the species remained exactly the same for a long time, and were then changed suddenly, and greatly, by some change in the world — such as the climate.

It is difficult to know the truth about the development of life on an earth that has existed for millions of years. Perhaps Darwin was right, perhaps he was wrong. But the fact that scientists all over the world believe that the world is millions of years old, and not only 6000 years old, is mainly because of Darwin's research and ideas. It is interesting to consider what would have happened if he had become a clergyman, as his father wanted.

Exercises

Comprehension

A Each of the following sentences describes a person mentioned in the book: give the names of each person.

1 The French scientist, born in 1707, who suspected that not all creatures were perfectly adapted to their environment.
2 The clergyman who wrote about the natural history of Selborne.
3 The man who didn't like Charles's nose.
4 The clergyman who wrote about population.
5 The man that Darwin sent Wallace's paper to.
6 The publisher of Darwin's books.
7 The man who gave a good review of *The Origin of Species*.
8 A famous anatomist, who changed from a friend of Darwin to an enemy.
9 Darwin's wife.
10 The man from Moravia who found an answer that Darwin didn't find.

B Each of these sentences describes an animal mentioned in the book: give the name of each animal.

11 A South American rodent with large ancestors.
12 Darwin collected these when he was a student.
13 A South American ostrich (or similar) that Darwin ate and then studied.
14 The insect carrying Chagas's disease.
15 There were thirteen kinds of this in the Galapagos Islands.

C Questions:
16 Why did Darwin study to become a clergyman?
17 Why did he join the crew of the *Beagle*?
18 What did the earthquake teach both Darwin and Fitzroy?
19 What surprised Darwin about the difference between the animals on the Galapagos Islands, and those in South America?
20 What was the importance of the book *The Origin of Species*, when it first appeared?

Language practice
1 Without looking back at the text you have read, try to fill in the missing words, which have all appeared in the book:

> The idea of natural . . . hit Charles like a . . . of lightning. He had realised the how of evolution and it was a new . . . . If the environment of the . . . changed, then some members would have to . . . to the new environment so they could . . . . This was the idea of the survival of the . . . and it explained how many species did not die . . ., as

the world changed, but became different.
2 The following sentences are quotations from the speech of Huxley and Bishop Wilberforce at the meeting in Oxford. Re-write the sentences as reported speech, as if in a news report:

'Is it through your grandfather or your grandmother that you are descended from a monkey?'
'If I had an ape for a grandfather, would it change my present morality and responsibilities? I tell you this: if I had to choose for a grandfather either an ape or an educated bishop who uses clever words to bring ridicule into a scientific discussion — then I would prefer an ape.'

Writing
1 What do you think was the most important new idea that Darwin had? Explain what it is and why it is important.
2 Why do you think many people disagreed (and continue to do so) with Darwin's ideas? Did/do they have good reasons? Explain your opinions.
3 Imagine you are in the same room as Darwin and Bishop Wilberforce, arguing about evolution, apes, God etc. Write down some of the conversation you think they have.
4 What effect has Darwin (and his ideas) had upon life and thinking in the 20th century? Summarise what different groups think.
5 What do different religions teach about Darwin's ideas? Do they think he is right or wrong about

history? Give a summary of what ideas they have.

6   Imagine you are Charles Darwin, returning from a trip to collect fossils. Write what you think he would write in his diary, sitting in his cabin in the *Beagle* in South America.

Activities

1   Look at the family tree on the next page: fill in the empty spaces with the names from the book.

2   Look at the quiz on page 76: find out the names of all the places mentioned here, which come from the book. Use a map to help.

3   The book mentions other theories of evolution. Find out what they are; find out what the theories of the paleontologists are, and how they are different from Darwin.

4   Take one of the animal examples from the book and try to find out how this animal evolved — what type of animals were its ancestors, how has it changed, what changes were there in the environment to cause this?

5   Find out the reactions to and beliefs about evolution in your own country and your own religion: do people think that Darwin was right, wrong, or a little of both? How do people explain the history of the world and of the living things in it?

Family Tree

Supply the names which should go in the boxes numbered 1 to 7

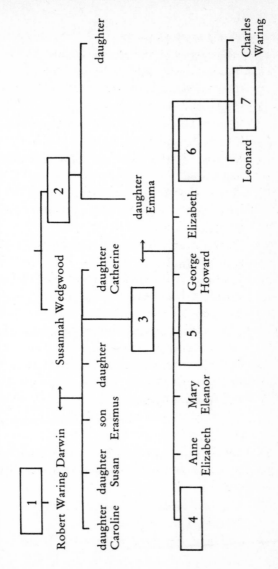

Activity 2 – Place Quiz

Give the names of the places.

1 The mountain where Noah's ark came to rest.
2 The native land of Jean Baptiste Lamarck.
3 The house where Charles spent his childhood.
4 The town where Charles went to school.
5 Charles's second university.
6 Where Charles went on trips with the Scottish fishermen.
7 Where the *Beagle* was built.
8 The islands where cholera stopped Charles from landing.
9 The first place where Charles set foot on land after leaving England.
10 Charles and Sims Covington make their first discovery of prehistoric bones on a beach. Name the country.
11 The mountains where Charles found marine fossils miles from the sea.
12 The town destroyed by an earthquake.
13 The island where Charles killed a fox with his geological hammer.
14 The homeland of Jemmy Button and York Minster.
15 The islands whose name means 'tortoises'.
16 The nearest mainland country to the Galapagos Islands.
17 The last continent visited by the *Beagle* before returning to England.
18 The *Beagle*'s port of arrival in Britain.

19 A group of islands in the Indian Ocean visited by the *Beagle*.
20 The name of the London street where Charles first lived as a married man.
21 The name of the house where Charles spent most of his adult life.
22 Where Alfred Wallace was living when he sent his ideas on natural selection to Charles.
23 The town of the famous meeting where T H Huxley and Soapy Sam publicly discussed Charles's ideas.
24 The present-day country which contains Gregor Mendel's homeland.
25 The only European country that Charles visited.
26 Charles's burial place.

Glossary

(to) acquire   To get, gain.

acre   A measurement of land; ca 4000 sq. metres.

(to) adapt   To change, to become more suitable.

Admiralty   The administration of the Navy.

anatomy   The study of animal and human bodies.

Andes   The highest mountains in South America.

angel   God's helper.

ape   An animal like a monkey, but taller; related to
   man.

aristocrat   A person from high or royal families.

basis   Foundation; main principle of an idea.

beagle   A small hunting dog.

beetle   An insect with a hard, shiny, black body.

Bible   The Christian book of God's words.

biology   The study of life and its forms.

bishop   An important man of the church.

bison   American buffalo.

blank   Something empty

(to) blend   To mix, change from one to another.

boarding school   A school where the pupils also stay
   to sleep.

botanic   Connected with the study of plants.

breeding Keeping animals or plants to produce new types of offspring.

cabin A room in a ship.

captain The leader of a ship.

capybara South American rodent.

carefree Happy, not worried.

catastrophe A sudden happening of destruction — fire, flood etc.

ceramics The making of pots.

chapter A part of a book.

characteristic A typical mark or quality of something.

chemistry The study of elements, solids, liquids.

cholera A disease found in hot countries.

classification The organisation of things according to their type.

clergyman A man of the church.

clinics The teaching of medicine at the hospital bedside.

coelacanth A large primitive fish, thought to be extinct 70 million years ago, until a living one was caught in 1938.

colonial When one country is controlled by another.

constantly Always.

(to) contribute To give something useful.

contribution What you give.

contributor A person who gives something useful.

(to) descend from To come from (your ancestors in the past).

descendants Your children's children's children etc.

destruction The breaking up/ruin of something.

dictator A leader with absolute and often cruel power.

dinosaurs Very large extinct reptiles.

disgrace Shame, loss of honour and pride.

dissection The cutting up of dead bodies or plants etc. for study.

domestication (of animals) Living with man e.g. cat, dog, horse.

earthquake A violent movement of the earth.

ecology The study of the biological relationships between living things.

ecosystem How these relationships are organised.

edition The form in which a book is published.

elephant The largest four-footed animal now living.

environment The surroundings and way in which a creature lives.

eruption Bursting out of a volcano.

evidence The proof or signs of proof.

evolution Development and change (gradual and slow).

(to) evolve To change, adapt, develop into something complex.

extinct Dead for ever; there will be no more of this type.

fascinated Interested and excited by.

financial To do with money.

finch A type of small bird.

fossil The remains, found in rock, of very old animals.

fox A wild animal, like a dog, with a large tail.

gaucho A South American cowboy.

generations Stages in a family; parents + children = 2 generations.

geography The study of the climate, form and uses of the earth.

geology The study of the earth's rocks and their history.

giraffe An African animal with a long neck.

goat A small mountain animal with horns.

guanaco A South American animal, like a camel.

iguana A large type of lizard.

inheritance The passing on of gifts/qualities from parents to children.

interpretation An explanation, the meaning seen in something.

laboratory A room for doing scientific experiments.

lash One hit with a whip or rope on someone's back.

lecture A class at university.

lieutenant An officer in the navy, below the captain.

literal Word-for-word, accepting every word as absolutely true.

logical Well-reasoned.

mammals Animals with hot blood, where the mother feeds the young with milk.

marine Produced by the sea.

mathematics The study of numbers.

microscope An instrument for looking at very small things.

missionary A person who tries to change other

people's religion to his own.

monkey   A small animal that looks like a man.

naturalist   A person who studies nature.

navy   A group of ships belonging to a country.

obsessed with   Cannot stop thinking about/doing.

obsession   What you cannot stop doing.

occasional   Something you do sometimes is occasional.

offspring   Children of animals.

Opticks (now Optics)   Study of light and seeing.

origin   The place where something came from.

orthodox   Accepting the general, normal ideas; not different.

ostrich   A large bird with a long neck which it puts in the sand.

patient   A person having medical treatment.

phenomenon   Something happening, often strange; plural phenomena.

philosophy   The study of knowledge and truth.

preservation   Keeping something alive.

previous   Earlier.

primitive   Simple, not civilised.

principle   A general law or truth.

(to) publish   To make and sell books.

reptile   A cold-blooded animal, which lays eggs eg. a snake, tortoise.

research   An original study and scientific investigation.

(to) review   To give an opinion of a book.

rhinoceros   A large African animal, thick-skinned,

with a horn on its nose.

ridicule Making something appear foolish and good enough only to be laughed at.

rodent A class of small mammals with strong front teeth.

selection Choosing; preference; choosing one thing rather than another.

shilling A coin in the old British system of money; now 5 pence.

significant Important; noteworthy; having meaning.

skeleton The bone framework of an animal.

skull The head-bone of an animal; the bone giving the head its shape.

slaves People belonging to an owner; people working for their owner without free choice.

sloth A slow-moving South American mammal which lives in trees.

species (sing. and pl.) The group of individual creatures having common marks and qualities.

specimen An individual example; a part of something to represent the whole.

spontaneously By itself; without help.

strict Difficult, demanding respect and authority.

summarise Say briefly; say in a few words.

surgery The science of fighting disease etc. by operations.

survey To inspect and measure land.

surveyor A person who does this.

(to) survive To continue living; remain alive.

survival Staying alive; continuing this form of animal.

temple A building used for religious services.

tendency An inclination; turning; leaning.

theory An explained idea based on one or more principles; a connected series of reasoned arguments.

tortoise A class of reptiles which have a hollow shell covering the body except for head, legs and tail.

traditional (of habits and customs) Handed down, or passed on, from previous generations.

tropical Of that part of the earth 23°27′ on either side of the equator.

volcano A hill or mountain from which gases, liquids, ashes etc. pour, coming from below the earth's surface.

voyage A journey made on water, particularly a long journey by ship.

zoology The science of the forms and distributions of animals.

Appendix 1

The People in the Story

This list does not include every person on board the *Beagle* during the famous voyage. That list is in Chapter Three of this book. Nor does it include the writer of every book mentioned in the story.

John James Audubon 1785–1851 American naturalist and painter

Fuegia Basket Fuegian, returning to her homeland on the *Beagle*

Comte Georges Leclerc de Buffon 1707–1788 French scientist

Dr Samuel Butler Headmaster at Shrewsbury School when Charles was a pupil there

Jemmy Button Fuegian, returning to his homeland on the *Beagle*

Lord George Gordon Byron 1788–1824 English romantic poet

Mr Case headmaster of the first school attended by Charles

Charles II King of England from 1660 to 1685

Sims Covington boy fiddler on board the *Beagle*, who became Charles's assistant

Anne Elizabeth Darwin 1840–1851 daughter of Charles and Emma

Charles Darwin 1809–1882 scientist

Charles Waring Darwin 1856–1859 son of Charles and Emma

Elizabeth Darwin born 1847 daughter of Charles and Emma

Erasmus Darwin 1731–1802 physician and writer, grandfather of Charles and father of Robert Waring

Erasmus Darwin 1804–1881 brother of Charles

Francis Darwin 1848–1925 son of Charles and Emma

George Howard Darwin 1845–1912 son of Charles and Emma

Henrietta Emma Darwin born 1843 daughter of Charles and Emma

Horace Darwin 1851–1928 son of Charles and Emma

Leonard Darwin 1850–1943 son of Charles and Emma

Mary Eleanor Darwin 1842–1842 daughter of Charles and Emma

Robert Waring Darwin 1766–1848 physician, son of Erasmus and father of Charles

William Erasmus Darwin 1839–1914 son of Charles and Emma

Robert Fitzroy 1805–1865 seaman, surveyor, meteorologist, captain of the *Beagle* and friend of Charles

George III King of England from 1760 to 1820

George IV King of England from 1820–1830

Robert Grant zoologist, and friend of Charles in Edinburgh

J S Henslow 1796–1861 teacher of Charles at Cambridge, writer, friend of Charles, and chairman of the Oxford meeting

Joseph Hooker 1817–1911 scientist and friend of Charles

Alexander von Humboldt 1769–1859 German scientist, traveller and writer

Thomas Henry Huxley 1825–1895 scientist and friend of Charles; defended Charles at the Oxford meeting

Jean Baptiste Lamarck 1744–1829 French scientist who had a theory of evolution

Sir Charles Lyell 1797–1875 geologist and friend of Charles, author of *Principles of Geology*

Thomas Malthus 1766–1835 clergyman, writer on population

Richard Matthews missionary on the *Beagle* who intended to stay with the Fuegians

William McGillivray 1796–1852 Scottish naturalist and writer

Gregor Mendel 1822–1884 Moravian clergyman and scientist; discovered the theory of heredity

York Minster Fuegian, returning to his homeland on the *Beagle*

John Murray 1808–1892 publisher of Charles's books

Sir Isaac Newton 1642–1727 English scientist

Noah   character in 'Genesis' who saved all living creatures from extinction by catastrophe

Richard Owen   1804–1892   anatomist and enemy of Charles's ideas

William Paley   1743–1805   clergyman and author of *Evidences for Christianity* (1794)

Sir Walter Scott   1771–1832   Scottish writer of novels and poems

Adam Sedgwick   1785–1837   geologist, teacher and friend of Charles at Cambridge; later enemy of Charles's ideas

William Shakespeare   1564–1616   English writer of plays and poems

Pringle Stokes   captain of the *Beagle* on her first South American voyage

Alfred Russel Wallace   1822–1913   naturalist and traveller; co-discoverer of the theory of natural selection

Emma Wedgwood   daughter of Uncle Jos, cousin and wife of Charles

Josiah Wedgwood (Uncle Jos)   1769–1843   father of Emma, brother of Charles' mother

Susannah Wedgwood   1766–1817   mother of Charles, wife of Robert Waring

Gilbert White   1720–1793   clergyman, author of *The Natural History of Selborne*

John Wickham   first lieutenant on the *Beagle*, friend of Charles during the voyage

Samuel Wilberforce (Soapy Sam)   1805–1873   Bishop of Oxford who spoke against Charles at the Oxford meeting

York Minster   Fuegian, returning to his homeland on the *Beagle*.

Appendix 2

Books
The books below are some of the books used in the preparation of this reader.
You may like to read more about Charles Darwin; this list may be a helpful starting point.

Charles Darwin and his World
Julian Huxley & H B D Kettlewell
Thames & Hudson 1965

Charles Darwin and The Origin of Species
the editors of Horizon Magazine & Walter Karp
Cassell 1968

Charles Darwin
Gavin de Beer
Thomas Nelson & Sons Ltd 1963

Gregor Mendel, Father of the Science of Genetics
Harry Sootin
Blackie 1961

What Darwin Really Said
Benjamin Farrington
Macdonald 1966

Darwin's Century
Loren Eiseley
Victor Gollancz 1959

The Narrative of the Voyage of the Beagle
Fitzroy, Darwin *et al.*; compiled by David Stanbury
The Folio Society 1977

Darwin's Forgotten World
Roger Lewin & Sally Anne Thompson
Bison Books 1978

The Voyage of Charles Darwin
Darwin, edited by Christopher Ralling
BBC 1979

The Illustrated Origin of Species
Darwin, abridged and introduced by
Richard E Leakey
Faber & Faber 1979

Darwin and the Beagle
Alan Moorehead
Penguin 1978

Charles Darwin
John Chancellor
George Weidenfeld 1973